▶ ▶| 🔊 3:56 / 14:29

FGTeeV FAMILY BIOGRAPHY

 FGTeeV ✔
21.6M subscribers

👍 27K 👎 → SHARE •••

2.7M VIEWS • 1 MONTH AGO

Duddy, Moomy, Lexi, Mike, Chase, and Shawn are the stars of FGTeeV, one of the most popular family gaming YouTube channels in the world, and FV Family, which have a combined total of more than 33 million subscribers and 40 billion views. This family of six loves gaming, traveling, and spontaneous dance parties. To learn more, visit them on YouTube @FGTeeV and @FV Family.

2,249 Comments ☰ Sort by

YOU   Add a comment... *Love this Book!*

ISBN 978-0-06-334046-6

TYPOGRAPHY BY ERICA DE CHAVEZ WONG   23 24 25 26 27   RTLO   10 9 8 7 6 5 4 3 2 1   FIRST EDITION

OF TIME!

By FGTeeV
Illustrated by Miguel Díaz Rivas

CHARACTERS

DUDDY/DUDDZ/ DUDSTER

The fun-loving dad is always optimistic and wants to turn every bad situation into a funkadelic dance party! But will his gaming skills stand the test of time?

MOOMY

Moomy keeps the fun train from going off the rails, but she's also sweet, as you can see by her chocolate-chip freckle!

LEXI

The boss of the children, and oftentimes the brains—the master strategist who takes control with the confidence of her gaming know-how.

MIKE/ MICKSTER

The second-in-command. Mike respects Lexi's rules but that doesn't mean he always follows them. And he's the first to tell you he's somewhat of a genius himself!

CHASE/ DRIZZY

He's the fearless sharp-shooter of the family, whether he's wielding a bottle of relish or a jousting lance!

SHAWN

Shawn is curious about everything, which sure keeps the family on its toes and sometimes dodging dino dook. He also thinks everything is hilarious and that his dad is the greatest.

CHARACTERS

OLD DUDDY

He's like Duddy, but old! Wait a minute—TWO Duddies? Then which one is the greatest gamer of all time?

CECIL

A gaming brat who's always up for a game, anywhere and anyTIME. But cover your ears if he loses!

KING C-VIII

The ruthless and mysterious ruler from a long time in the future in a galaxy very close to ours who wants to be the greatest gamer of all time!

SEARCH AND FIND

SEE IF YOU CAN FIND THESE CHARACTERS THAT ARE HIDDEN THROUGHOUT THE BOOK. ANSWERS ON LAST PAGE.

MILO

Milo is the big man on the high school campus who is always by Lexi's side, and Duddy wishes he would go away. But Duddz should be careful what he wishes for.

PRINCE MYRON

Prince Myron looks like Milo, walks like Milo, talks like Milo . . . but though he is no Milo when it comes to bravery, he is all heart.

GRANDPA

Old grandpa is old and tells the same old stories and is old and falls asleep everywhere and is old.

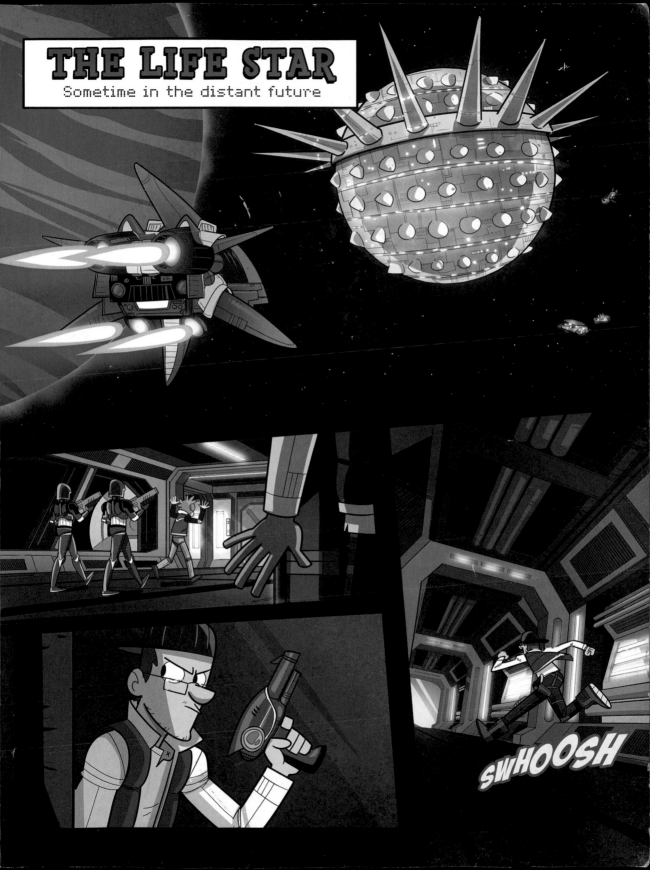

9

"**XYLE.** HE'S THIS GAMER WHO MESSAGED ME ON DISCORD OUT OF NOWHERE.

"HE TOLD ME HE HAD SOMETHING COOL TO SHOW ME . . .

" . . . SO WE AGREED TO MEET UP AT THIS **GAME STORE**. AT LEAST I THINK IT WAS A GAME STORE.

"IS A **OUIJA BOARD** A GAME? I DON'T KNOW. ANYWAYS . . .

"HE GAVE ME THIS WATCH. HE SAID IT WAS THE GAMING SYSTEM OF THE FUTURE. HE WANTED ME TO BE THE FIRST TO TEST IT.

I REALLY DID IT!

A MILLION POINTS! A MILLION POINTS!

I WONDER WHAT'S GOING TO HAPPEN! "AN ACHIEVEMENT BEYOND MY WILDEST IMAGINATION!" **WHAT COULD IT BE?**

OKAY, I'VE HAD ENOUGH OF YOU AND THAT SILLY WATCH.

KIDS—

—GET IT OFF OF HIM!

WHAT? NO!

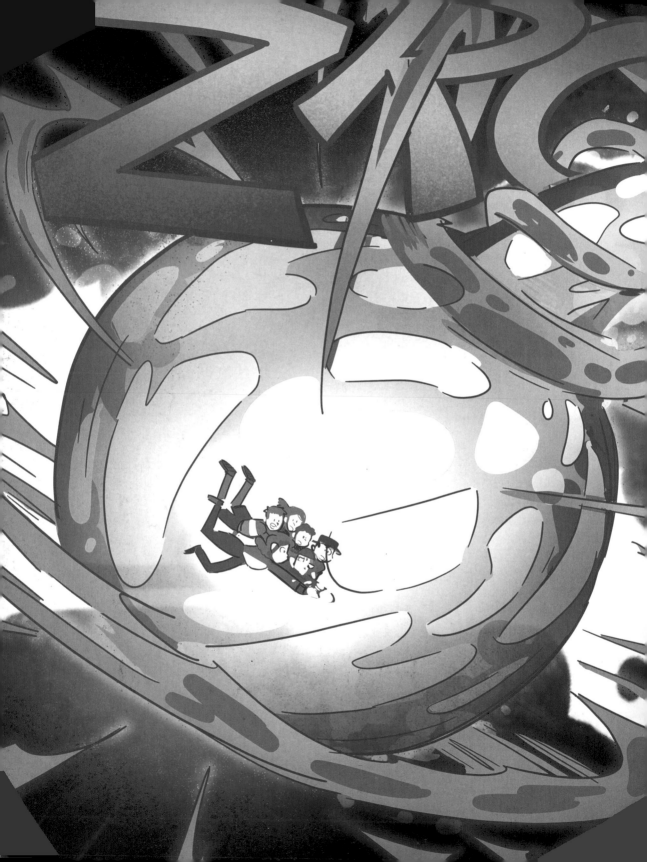

LEAVE IT **LOST**. THAT THING HAS BEEN NOTHING BUT TROUBLE.

LET'S GO TO THE REN FAIRE AND FIGURE OUT WHERE WE ARE.

I'M NOT GOING WITHOUT MY EWATCH!

I'M GONNA ASK THOSE PEEPS IF THEY'VE SEEN IT.

SCUSE ME—?

GOOD MORROW TO YOU, SIR!

SUP? HAVE EITHER OF YOU SEEN A **WATCH**? I LOST MINE.

A "WATCH"? LIKE A **GUARD**?

NO, LIKE A **WRIST**WAT— OH, I GET IT.

THE EWATCH MUST HAVE SENT US INTO A TIME **VORTEX**! IT TRANSPORTED US TO THE TIME OF ITS MIDDLE AGES GAME— EXCEPT IT'S **NOT A GAME**!

ARE WE GONNA HAVE TO LEARN TO TALK FUNNY?

FEAR NOT, SIR MIKE—I SHALL TEACHETH YOU!

I CAN'T LIVE IN THE MIDDLE AGES! DO YOU KNOW WHAT KIND OF A PLACE IT WAS FOR YOUNG WOMEN LIKE ME? THEY HAD MORE RULES THAN **DUDDY** DOES!

OF ALL THE GAMES ON YOUR WATCH, IT HAD TO TAKE US TO **THIS** ONE?

TRUST ME, SHAWN. IT COULD HAVE BEEN **WORSE**.

IT'S OKAY. **WE'RE** OKAY. ALL WE NEED TO DO IS FIND THE EWATCH AND USE IT TO GET BACK HOME.

I THOUGHT YOU WANTED TO LEAVE IT LOST.

I MIGHT LEAVE **YOU** LOST IF YOU'RE GONNA BE A WISE GUY. COME ON—

"—LET'S GO FIND YOUR WATCH."

LOOK, MOOMY—A **PET STORE**!

UH, YEAH, THAT'S WHAT IT IS—A **PET STORE**.

UH ... WE'D BETTER KEEP MOVING.

I FOUND THIS BRACELET IN THE MEADOW.

THE MEADOW...?

MY **EWATCH**!

IT SURE HAS A **SHINE** TO IT! IT'S UNLIKE ANY METAL I HAVE EVER SEEN!

SPLENDID! I SHALL GIVE YOU **TWENTY SHILLINGS** FOR IT!

GOOD, ER, **MORROW**, SIR— BUT THAT'S MY **WATCH** YOU'VE GOT THERE. . .

THE NAME IS LORD MANIFESTO. AND I JUST **PAID TWENTY SHILLINGS** FOR IT, SO IT'S ACTUALLY **MY** BRACELET. UNLESS, OF COURSE, YOU WISH TO **BUY** IT FROM **ME**. WHAT SAY YOU TO **THIRTY SHILLINGS**?

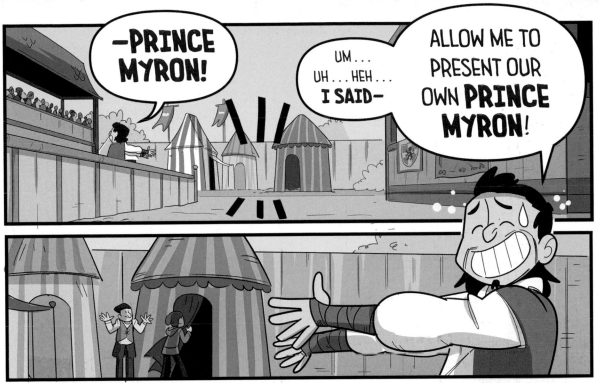

YOU HAVE TO GIVE HIM MORE TIME! WE **NEED** THAT WATCH.

I'M AFRAID A DEAL'S A DEAL!

GOOD PEOPLE, I HAVE AN ANNOUNCEMENT—

BY ORDER OF THE KING AND QUEEN, THE MATCH HAS BEEN **POSTPONED** SO THAT HIS HIGHNESS PRINCE MYRON CAN HAVE TIME TO ARRIVE AT THE ARENA.

WHEW! YOU HEARD THE MAN! THE BET'S NOT OVER YET!

HARRUMPH. THEY HAD BETTER NOT GIVE THAT SPOILED BRAT **TOO** MUCH TIME.

IS THAT PRINCE MYRON'S CASTLE OVER THERE?

WHY, YES, YOUNG LADY. IT IS.

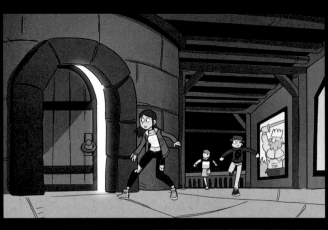

PRINCE MYRON?

BARTHOLOMEW? **FINALLY!** COME IN! HURRY!

MILO?!

YOU'RE NOT **BARTHOLOMEW!**

WHO IS **MILO?**

Y-YOU LOOK **JUST LIKE** SOMEONE I KNOW. YOU MUST BE AN **ANCESTOR** OR SOMETHING!

WHAT IS THE MEANING OF THIS? WHO ART THOU? **GUARDS!**

QUIET DOWN, PRINCE! I'VE GOT THREE-DAY-OLD **GYM SOCKS** IN MY HAND, AND I'M NOT AFRAID TO USE THEM!

GAH! THE **FOUL STENCH** IS BURNING MY NOSE HAIRS! MY **EYES** ARE WATERING! WHAT DO YOU **WANT** WITH ME?

WHY NOT?

DON'T MAKE ME USE THE SOCKS AGAIN!

WE NEED YOU TO GET TO THE ARENA FOR YOUR JOUST **RIGHT AWAY!**

WHAT? BUT— BUT—BUT—I CANNOT JOUST!

BECAUSE I'M AFRAID!

THAT WAS **TOO CLOSE A CALL**!

WHOA! DUDDZ!

YOU HAVE A **SWEET 'STACHE**!

I–I DO! IT'S— IT'S EVERYTHING I EVER WANTED!

YOU'D BETTER **GIT** IF YOU KNOW WHAT'S GOOD FOR YA!

I SAID THIS TOWN AIN'T BIG ENOUGH FOR THE TWO OF US.

BUT DON'T YOU KNOW WHAT YOUR MUSTACHE MEANS?

I'M GONNA START COUGHING UP **HAIR BALLS**?

WE ALTERED THE **TIMELINE**!

"GRANDPA"?!

OH! UM . . . I MEAN . . . THAT **GUY** OVER THERE—HE LOOKS LIKE MY **GRANDPA**.

ISN'T THAT GUY KINDA YOUNG TO BE YOUR **GRANDPA**?

NOT IF WE TIME TRAVELED FROM THE FUTURE.

TIME TRAVELED?! YOU'RE A FUNNY GUY, UH . . .

CALL ME "DUDDZ." EVERYONE DOES.

IT'S NICE TO MEET YOU, DUDDZ. FEEL FREE TO STICK AROUND AND HAVE SOME PUNCH!

WILL DO, GRAND—ER, **ANTOINE**!

WHAT ARE YOU DOING? WE CAN'T STAY! WE ALREADY MESSED WITH THE TIMELINE ENOUGH.

IS THAT REALLY **GRANDPA**?

THIS IS MY CHANCE TO SEE THE STORIES **BEHIND** THE STORIES. WHEN GRANDPA TELLS THEM THEY SEEM SO LAME, BUT LOOK AT HOW **COOL** THIS IS!

WHO KNEW?

WE'LL STAY FOR JUST A FEW MINUTES.

HOW MUCH HARM COULD WE POSSIBLY DO IN **JUST A FEW MINUTES**?

THIS IS **SO COOL**.

DO YOU **SURF** TOO?

HM? SURE. ALL THE TIME.

WHY DIDN'T YOU EVER **TELL** ME THAT?

WE JUST MET **FIVE MINUTES AGO**.

OH. RIGHT. WHAT I'M SAYING IS, IF I WERE A SURFER, I'D TALK ABOUT THAT **ALL THE TIME**, EVEN WHEN I GOT OLD.

NAH. PEOPLE WOULD GET KIND OF TIRED OF HEARING THE SAME STORIES OVER AND OVER AGAIN.

YEAH, I . . . I GUESS YOU'RE RIGHT.

HEY . . .

. . . WHAT ARE YOU **LOOKING** AT?

THE ONLY THING **WORTH** LOOKING AT ON THIS BEACH . . .

HER.

IS THAT **GRAMMY**?

HER NAME'S **PATRICE**. I'VE BEEN TRYING TO FIND THE COURAGE TO ASK HER OUT FOR A SODA FOR **WEEKS**.

BUT THIS TIME I'M FINALLY GONNA DO IT—

BECAUSE YOU HAVE YOUR **LUCKY PENNY**!

HOW'D YOU **KNOW** THAT?

UH, ER, I, UH ... IT'S AN OLD CUSTOM WHERE I COME FROM.

HEY, LET ME GO GET YOU A REFILL ON THAT PUNCH!

75

ALL RIGHT, I TRIED TO BE **NICE**, BUT YOU DONE DID IT NOW.

WHERE I COME FROM, THERE'S ONLY **ONE WAY** TO SETTLE SITUATIONS LIKE THIS—

—A RAP BATTLE!

RAP? WHAT?

YO, DJ MICKSTER— **GIVE ME A BEAT!**

PBBT! PT! PBBT PBBT PBBT **PT!**

LUCKY PENNY, HERE WE GO!

HEY, PATRICE, I'VE BEEN MEANING TO ASK YOU—

DO YOU GUYS **HEAR** THAT? IT'S COMING FROM THE **PARKING LOT**.

LET'S GO CHECK IT OUT!

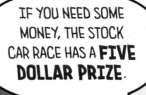

YOU WORKED THREE MONTHS AT YOUR DAD'S USED CAR LOT. BLAH, BLAH, BLAH! I'VE HEARD THE STORY A GAZILLION TIMES.

I NEED A CROWN AND I HAVE **NO CASH** TO BUY ANOTHER WATCH!

IF YOU NEED SOME MONEY, THE STOCK CAR RACE HAS A **FIVE DOLLAR PRIZE**.

THAT WOULD HIT **TWO** BIRDS WITH **ONE CAR**, WOULDN'T IT? EXCEPT I DON'T HAVE A CAR.

UNLESS . . .

. . . YOU LET ME **BORROW** ONE FROM YOUR DAD'S LOT?

WHAT? NO WAY! MY DAD WOULD GROUND ME FOR LIFE!

H-HOW DID YOU KNOW . . . ?

YOU'RE NOT GONNA **TELL** ON ME, ARE YOU?

LET'S DISCUSS IT ON THE WAY TO THE LOT!

COME ON. IT'S NOT LIKE **YOU'VE** NEVER BORROWED A CAR. LIKE THAT TIME YOU HIT THE MILLERS' MAILBOX AND BLAMED IT ON THE GARBAGE TRUCK . . .

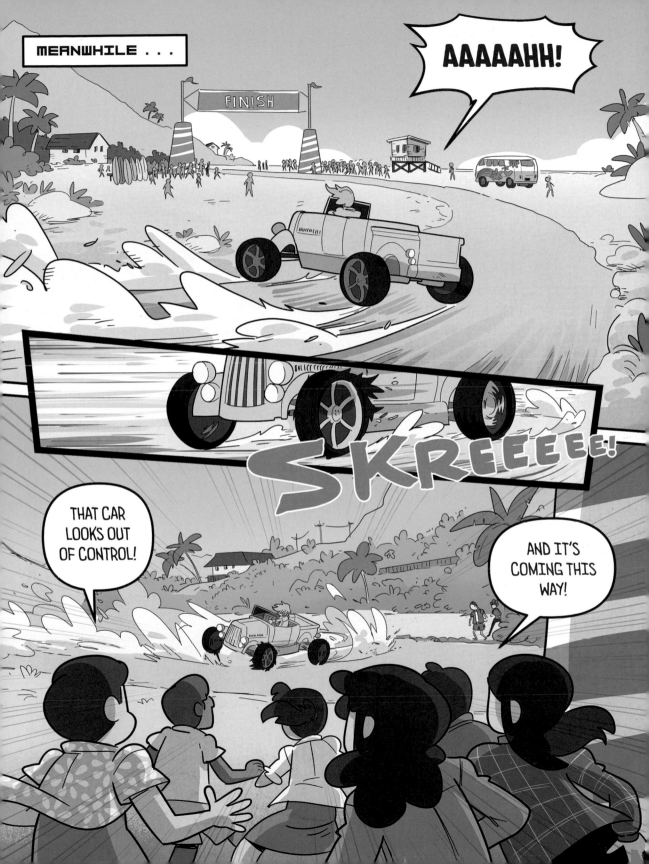

121

RRGH!

YOU THINK I HAVE A **DEATH WISH**? I'M NOT GONNA CHASE AFTER THEM WITH THAT THING!

RRGH?

I'VE GOT A **BETTER IDEA**.

WE'RE GONNA PUT TOGETHER A **STRATEGY** AND GET AT IT LIKE WE'RE PLAYING A VIDEO GAME . . .

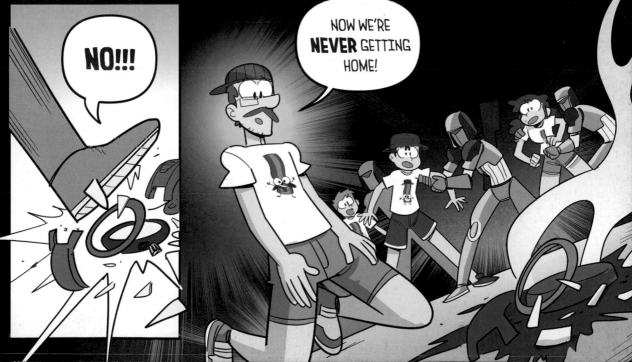

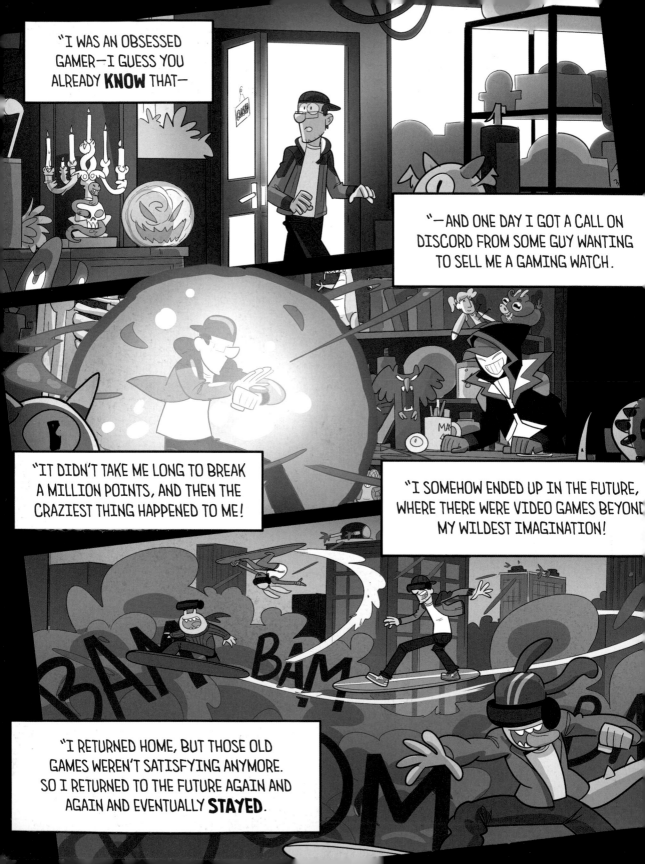

"I STILL HAVE MY OLD EWATCH—BUT IT'S WITH MY STUFF AT THE ROLLING HILLS HOME FOR REALLY OLD GAMERS . . . ON THE LIFE STAR."

BUT WE JUST SAID THAT NO ONE CAN SOLVE THE INFINITE CASTLE.

ACTUALLY . . . I THINK I CAN!

HOW?

"ONE OF THE USELESS FACTS I LEARNED FOR THE **ACADEMIC BEE** WAS THE GREEK MYTH ABOUT **THESEUS**.

"THESEUS HAD TO SOLVE AN IMPOSSIBLE MAZE CALLED A LABYRINTH TO FIND AND DEFEAT A BEAST CALLED THE **MINOTAUR**."

<YAWN> JUST THINKING ABOUT THAT ACADEMIC BEE IS MAKING ME BORED ALL OVER AGAIN.

GO ON.

"THESEUS SOLVED THE MAZE BY TYING A STRING TO THE ENTRANCE AND LETTING IT OUT AS HE WALKED.

"SO ALL HE HAD TO DO WAS FOLLOW THE STRING BACK OUT!"

WHAT GOOD DOES THAT DO US? WE DON'T HAVE ANY STRING!

WE DON'T **NEED** ANY. WE JUST HAVE TO FIND A WAY TO MARK THE HALLWAYS WE'VE ALREADY BEEN DOWN.

MARK THEM WITH **WHAT**?

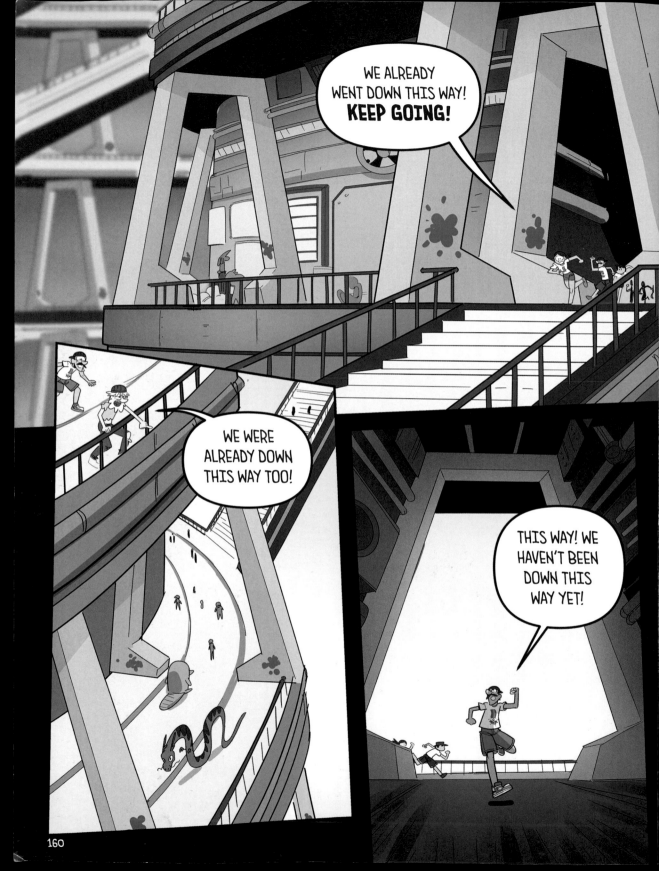

163

TELL THEM!

TELL THEM HOW YOU'RE A BIG **CHEATER**, AND IT'S NOT FAIR!

I BEAT YOU **FAIR AND SQUARE!**

VINCENT...? WHAT'S HE TALKING ABOUT?

REMEMBER HOW I TOLD YOU I HAD AN APPRENTICE? WELL, I GAVE HIM A CHANCE TO PLAY ME TO SEE WHICH ONE OF US IS THE GREATEST GAMER **OF ALL TIME**.

AFTER HE LOST, HE HAD SUCH A TEMPER TANTRUM THAT HE OVERTHREW THE REPUBLIC AND NAMED HIMSELF THE EMPEROR.

HE WAS A REAL **GAMER BRAT!**

A... **WHAT?!**

IT'S TRUE...

187

ZROOOSHT
THERE'S THE SCHOOL!
WE REALLY ACTUALLY **FINALLY** MADE IT HOME!
AND WE FIXED THE **TIMELINE**!
SEE? WE'RE BACK TO OUR **OLD SELVES**!
CHASE
AND YOUR **MUSTACHE** IS GONE!
NO WONDER MY UPPER LIP FEELS SO **COLD** RIGHT NOW.
YOU SHOULD GROW IT BACK! IT WAS **CUTE**!

HEY, EVERYBODY! ARE YOU ALL READY FOR **FAMILY GAME NIGHT**?

YO, WHERE IS EVERYBODY? THIS PLACE LOOKS LIKE **DOGGY DAY CARE**.

YOU JUST MISSED EVERYONE. **SHAWN** IS AT A **SLEEPOVER** AND **MIKE** AND **CHASE** ARE AT THE MALL.

HEH. THE MALL.

DID WE MAKE THAT PLACE **COOL** AGAIN?

199

THE END.

SEARCH AND FIND ANSWER KEY:

GUNKEY TURKEY [PAGE 30]; SCARED GUNKEY TURKEY [PAGE 58]; FUNNEL BOY [PAGE 83]; DERPY BACON AND WEGGS [PAGE 98]; NEIL [PAGE 108]; BARGO BEANS [PAGE 33]; APE CHASE [PAGE 53]; BLOBBY FISH [PAGE 138]; GOOSY DUDDY [PAGE 2]; FLY AND TURD [PAGE 18]